ELSEVIER

Season's Greetings

Academic Press • Butterworth-Heinemann • Cell Press • Churchill Livingstone
Engineering Information • Excerpta Medica • The Lancet • MDConsult • MDL
Mosby • North-Holland • Pergamon • ScienceDirect • WB Saunders

diary
kalender
agenda
2005

Dolls' Houses
Maisons de Poupée
Puppenhäuser
Poppenhuizen

2005

01
	53	01	02	03	04	05
		03	10	17	24	31
		04	11	18	25	
		05	12	19	26	
		06	13	20	27	
		07	14	21	28	
	01	08	15	22	29	
	02	09	16	23	30	

02
	05	06	07	08	09
		07	14	21	28
	01	08	15	22	
	02	09	16	23	
	03	10	17	24	
	04	11	18	25	
	05	12	19	26	
	06	13	20	27	

03
	09	10	11	12	13
		07	14	21	28
	01	08	15	22	29
	02	09	16	23	30
	03	10	17	24	31
	04	11	18	25	
	05	12	19	26	
	06	13	20	27	

04
	13	14	15	16	17
		04	11	18	25
		05	12	19	26
		06	13	20	27
		07	14	21	28
	01	08	15	22	29
	02	09	16	23	30
	03	10	17	24	

05
	17	18	19	20	21	22
		02	09	16	23	30
		03	10	17	24	31
		04	11	18	25	
		05	12	19	26	
		06	13	20	27	
		07	14	21	28	
	01	08	15	22	29	

06
	22	23	24	25	26
		06	13	20	27
		07	14	21	28
	01	08	15	22	29
	02	09	16	23	30
	03	10	17	24	
	04	11	18	25	
	05	12	19	26	

07
	26	27	28	29	30
		04	11	18	25
		05	12	19	26
		06	13	20	27
		07	14	21	28
	01	08	15	22	29
	02	09	16	23	30
	03	10	17	24	31

08
	31	32	33	34	35
	01	08	15	22	29
	02	09	16	23	30
	03	10	17	24	31
	04	11	18	25	
	05	12	19	26	
	06	13	20	27	
	07	14	21	28	

09
	35	36	37	38	39
		05	12	19	26
		06	13	20	27
		07	14	21	28
	01	08	15	22	29
	02	09	16	23	30
	03	10	17	24	
	04	11	18	25	

10
	39	40	41	42	43	44
		03	10	17	24	31
		04	11	18	25	
		05	12	19	26	
		06	13	20	27	
		07	14	21	28	
	01	08	15	22	29	
	02	09	16	23	30	

11
	44	45	46	47	48
		07	14	21	28
	01	08	15	22	29
	02	09	16	23	30
	03	10	17	24	
	04	11	18	25	
	05	12	19	26	
	06	13	20	27	

12
	48	49	50	51	52
		05	12	19	26
		06	13	20	27
		07	14	21	28
	01	08	15	22	29
	02	09	16	23	30
	03	10	17	24	31
	04	11	18	25	

personal details | memento personnel | persönliche daten | personalia

name   nom   naam

address   adresse   adres

postal code   code postal   postleitzahl   postcode

city   ville   ort   plaats

tel   tél

fax   télécopie   telefax

e-mail

place of work   bureau   arbeitsstelle   werk

address   adresse   adres

postal code   code postal   postleitzahl   postcode

city   ville   ort   plaats

tel   tél

fax   télécopie   telefax

e-mail

contact in case of emergency   prévenir en cas d'accident

bei unfall benachrichtigen   bij ongeval waarschuwen

name   nom   naam

address   adresse   adres

postal code   code postal   postleitzahl   postcode

city   ville   ort   plaats

tel   tél

2004

```
01    05 12 19 26        02    02 09 16 23          03 01 08 15 22 29     04    05 12 19 26
      06 13 20 27              03 10 17 24             02 09 16 23 30            06 13 20 27
      07 14 21 28              04 11 18 25             03 10 17 24 31            07 14 21 28
01 08 15 22 29                 05 12 19 26          04 11 18 25           01 08 15 22 29
02 09 16 23 30                 06 13 20 27          05 12 19 26           02 09 16 23 30
03 10 17 24 31                 07 14 21 28          06 13 20 27          03 10 17 24
04 11 18 25              01 08 15 22 29             07 14 21 28          04 11 18 25

05    03 10 17 24 31     06    07 14 21 28          07    05 12 19 26     08    02 09 16 23 30
      04 11 18 25        01 08 15 22 29                   06 13 20 27           03 10 17 24 31
      05 12 19 26        02 09 16 23 30                   07 14 21 28           04 11 18 25
      06 13 20 27        03 10 17 24             01 08 15 22 29                 05 12 19 26
      07 14 21 28        04 11 18 25             02 09 16 23 30                 06 13 20 27
01 08 15 22 29           05 12 19 26             03 10 17 24 31           07 14 21 28
02 09 16 23 30           06 13 20 27             04 11 18 25              01 08 15 22 29

09    06 13 20 27        10    04 11 18 25          11 01 08 15 22 29     12    06 13 20 27
      07 14 21 28              05 12 19 26             02 09 16 23 30           07 14 21 28
01 08 15 22 29                 06 13 20 27             03 10 17 24          01 08 15 22 29
02 09 16 23 30                 07 14 21 28          04 11 18 25            02 09 16 23 30
03 10 17 24             01 08 15 22 29             05 12 19 26            03 10 17 24 31
04 11 18 25             02 09 16 23 30             06 13 20 27            04 11 18 25
05 12 19 26             03 10 17 24 31             07 14 21 28            05 12 19 26
```

2006

```
01    02 09 16 23 30     02    06 13 20 27          03    06 13 20 27     04    03 10 17 24
      03 10 17 24 31           07 14 21 28                07 14 21 28           04 11 18 25
      04 11 18 25        01 08 15 22                01 08 15 22            05 12 19 26
      05 12 19 26        02 09 16 23                02 09 16 23 30         06 13 20 27
      06 13 20 27        03 10 17 24                03 10 17 24 31         07 14 21 28
      07 14 21 28        04 11 18 25                04 11 18 25           01 08 15 22 29
01 08 15 22 29           05 12 19 26                05 12 19 26           02 09 16 23 30

05 01 08 15 22 29        06    05 12 19 26          07    03 10 17 24 31   08    07 14 21 28
02 09 16 23 30                 06 13 20 27                04 11 18 25      01 08 15 22 29
03 10 17 24 31                 07 14 21 28                05 12 19 26      02 09 16 23 30
04 11 18 25              01 08 15 22 29                   06 13 20 27      03 10 17 24 31
05 12 19 26              02 09 16 23 30                   07 14 21 28      04 11 18 25
06 13 20 27              03 10 17 24             01 08 15 22 29            05 12 19 26
07 14 21 28              04 11 18 25             02 09 16 23 30            06 13 20 27

09    04 11 18 25        10    02 09 16 23 30       11    06 13 20 27     12    04 11 18 25
      05 12 19 26              03 10 17 24 31             07 14 21 28           05 12 19 26
      06 13 20 27              04 11 18 25          01 08 15 22 29              06 13 20 27
      07 14 21 28              05 12 19 26          02 09 16 23 30              07 14 21 28
01 08 15 22 29                 06 13 20 27          03 10 17 24           01 08 15 22 29
02 09 16 23 30                 07 14 21 28          04 11 18 25           02 09 16 23 30
03 10 17 24             01 08 15 22 29             05 12 19 26            03 10 17 24 31
```

general data

Address

Jan Luykenstraat 1, Amsterdam
Dependance museum and museumshop Schiphol Airport,
Holland Boulevard Schiphol between E and F pier

Postal address

Rijksmuseum, P.O. Box 74888, 1070 DN Amsterdam
Tel. +31 20-6747000 | 6747047
Fax +31 20-6747001
www.rijksmuseum.nl

Admission fees

Till age of 19   free
Adults   € 9.00
Groups (15 or more people)
Till age of 19   free
Adults   € 7.20

Opening hours

Daily 9.00 a.m. - 6.00 p.m.
Closed on 1 January
For evening openings: www.rijksmuseum.nl

How to reach the Rijksmuseum

Trams 2 and 5 (get off at Hobbemastraat)

Guided tours

Special guided tours in various languages are organized
on request. Price: on demand. There is a maximum
of 15 people per tour. Please apply at least four weeks
in advance, Tel. +31 20-6747191 | 6747194

On-line shop

http://shop.rijksmuseum.nl

informations generales

Adresse

Jan Luykenstraat 1, Amsterdam
Dependance de musée et de boutique Schiphol Airport,
Holland Boulevard Schiphol entre les passerelles E et F

Adresse postale

Rijksmuseum, Boîte postale 74888, 1070 DN Amsterdam
Tél. +31 20-6747000 | 6747047
Fax +31 20-6747001
www.rijksmuseum.nl

Prix d'entrée

Jusqu'a 19 ans   gratuit
Adultes   € 9.00
Prix de groupe (à partir de 15 personnes)
Jusqu'a 19 ans   gratuit
Adultes   € 7.20

Heures d'ouverture

Tous les jours de 9 heures à 18 heures
Fermé le 1er janvier
Pour des ouvertures du soir: www.rijksmuseum.nl

Comment s'y rendre

Tramway 2 et 5 (descendre à Hobbemastraat)

Visites guidées

Des visites guidées en différentes langues possible.
Prix: sur demande. Maximum 15 personnes. Prière
de faire la demande au moins quatre semaines d'avance,
Tel. +31 20-6747191 | 6747194

Boutique électronique

http://shop.rijksmuseum.nl

RIJKS MUSEUM
amsterdam

algemeine informationen

Besuchsadresse
Jan Luykenstraat 1, Amsterdam
Dependance Museum und Museumshop Schiphol Airport,
Holland Boulevard Schiphol zwischen Flugsteig E und F

Postadresse
Rijksmuseum, Postbus 74888, 1070 DN Amsterdam

Tel. +31 20-6747000 | 6747047

Fax: +31 20-6747001

www.rijksmuseum.nl

Eintrittspreise
Bis 19 Jahre   frei

Erwachsene   € 9.00

Preise für Gruppen (ab 15 Personen)

Bis 19 Jahre   frei

Erwachsene   € 7.20

Öffnungszeiten
Täglich von 9.00 - 18.00 Uhr

Am 1. Januar geschlossen

Für Öffnungzeiten am Abend: www.rijksmuseum.nl

Anreise mit öffentlichen Verkehrsmitteln
Straßenbahnlinien 2 und 5 (Halte Hobbemastraat)

Führungen
Auf Wunsch werden Sonderführungen in verschiedenen
Sprachen angeboten. Preis: auf Anfrage. Maximal 15 Personen.
Spätestens vier Wochen vor Museumsbesuch reservieren,
Tel. +31 20-6747191 | 6747194

On-line shop
http://shop.rijksmuseum.nl

algemene informatie

Bezoekadres
Jan Luykenstraat 1, Amsterdam
Dependance museum en museumshop Schiphol Airport,
Holland Boulevard Schiphol tussen E en F pier

Postadres
Rijksmuseum, Postbus 74888, 1070 DN Amsterdam

Tel. 020-6747000 | 6747047

Fax: 020-6747001

www.rijksmuseum.nl

Toegangsprijs
Tot 19 jaar   gratis

Volwassenen   € 9.00

Groepsprijzen (vanaf 15 personen)

Tot 19 jaar   gratis

Volwassenen   € 7.20

Toegang gratis voor Museumjaarkaarthouders

Openingstijden
Dagelijks van 9.00 - 18.00 uur

Gesloten op 1 januari

Voor avondopenstellingen: www.rijksmuseum.nl

Bereikbaarheid
Tram 2 en 5 (halte Hobbemastraat)

Rondleidingen
Speciale rondleidingen in diverse talen kunnen worden
aangevraagd. Prijs: op aanvraag. Maximaal 15 personen.
Minimaal vier weken voor het bezoek aanvragen,
Tel. 020-6747191 | 6747194

On-line shop
http://shop.rijksmuseum.nl

Dolls' Houses

Upstairs in the linen room are an old-fashioned linen press and a basket with linen clothes. Next to it, in the nursery, a little child lies on a splendid bedspread of cotton and silk. Downstairs in the cellar are storage jars with herbs.

In the house next to it, in a salon on the second floor, are some gorgeous walnut armchairs covered with silk velvet. One floor down, in the kitchen, you will find dishes with fruits made of wax. Made of wax? Yes, wax.

Because this is the 17th-century doll's house of Petronella Oortman. The house next to it is the doll's house of Petronella Dunois. Both showpiece doll's houses can be seen in the Rijksmuseum. They belong to the museum's major exhibits.

Visiting the two showpiece doll's houses gives you an excellent impression of the houses, clothing, people and objects from the 17th century. Some objects have been depicted so wonderfully and lifelike that it is hard to believe they are miniatures.

Please step inside!

Maisons de Poupée

Une presse à linge d'autrefois et un panier rempli de vêtements en lin se trouvent dans le grenier à vêtements. A côté du grenier, un enfant est allongé sur un magnifique couvre-lit de coton et de soie dans la chambre d'enfants. En bas, dans la cave, s'accumulent les bocaux contenant des herbes aromatiques.

Dans la maison d'à côté, au deuxième étage, de splendides sièges à accoudoirs en noyer revêtus de velours soyeux se dressent dans une salle somptueuse.

Si vous descendez un étage plus bas, dans la cuisine, vous trouverez des coupes de fruits en cire. En cire? Oui, en cire.

Il s'agit notamment de la maison de poupée de Petronella Oortman datant du 17e siècle. La maison d'à côté est la maison de poupée de Petronella Dunois. Ces deux maisons de poupée sont des joyaux que vous pourrez admirer au Rijksmuseum. Elles font partie des pièces les plus fameuses du musée.

Une visite à ces deux maisons de poupée vous donnera une magnifique impression des gens, des maisons, des vêtements et des objets utilisés au 17e siècle. Certains objets ont été réalisés avec une telle minutie et beauté qu'ils semblent réels et qu'il est presque inconcevable de savoir que ce sont des miniatures.

Soyez les bienvenus!

Puppenhäuser

Oben auf dem Dachboden, der als Leinenzimmer
dient, steht eine altmodische Leinenpresse und ein
Korb mit Kleidern. Nebenan im Kinderzimmer liegt
ein kleines Kind auf einer wunderschönen Bettdecke
aus Baumwolle und Seide. Unten im Keller befinden
sich Vorratsgefäße mit Kräutern.
Im Haus nebenan stehen im zweiten Stock mit
seidigem Samt bezogene Sessel mit Armlehnen aus
Nussbaumholz in einem luxuriösen Saal. Ein Stockwerk
tiefer stehen in der Küche Schüsseln mit Früchten
aus Wachs. Wie, aus Wachs? Genau richtig, aus Wachs.
Es ist nämlich das Puppenhaus von Petronella Oortman
aus dem siebzehnten Jahrhundert. Das daneben
stehende Haus ist das Puppenhaus von Petronella
Dunois. Beide Pracht-Puppenhäuser können im
Rijksmuseum bewundert werden. Sie gehören zu
den Glanzpunkten des Museums.
Durch den Besuch der prächtigen Puppenhäuser
bekommt man einen guten Eindruck von den
Häusern, der Kleidung, den Gegenständen und den
Menschen im siebzehnten Jahrhundert. Einige der
Gegenstände sind so schön und lebensecht, dass man
ganz dabei vergisst, dass es Miniaturen sind.
Treten Sie ein!

Poppenhuizen

Boven op de kleerzolder staan een ouderwetse
linnenpers en een mand met linnen kleertjes.
Daarnaast, in de kinderkamer, ligt een kindje op een
prachtig beddensprei van katoen en zijde. Beneden
in de kelder liggen voorraadpotten met kruiden.
In het huis ernaast, op de tweede verdieping, staan
in een luxe zaal beeldige armstoelen van notenhout
bekleed met zijden fluweel. Een verdieping lager,
in de keuken, vind je schotels met vruchten van was.
Van was? Ja, van was.
Dit is namelijk het 17e-eeuwse poppenhuis van
Petronella Oortman. Het huis hiernaast is het poppenhuis van Petronella Dunois. Beide pronkpoppenhuizen
zijn te bekijken in het Rijksmuseum. Ze behoren
tot de topstukken van het museum.
Bij een bezoek aan beide pronkpoppenhuizen krijg
je een prachtig beeld van de huizen, de kleding,
de mensen en de voorwerpen uit de 17e eeuw.
Sommige voorwerpen zijn zó mooi en levensecht
afgebeeld dat het nauwelijks voor te stellen is
dat het miniaturen zijn.
Treed binnen!

Dolls' house of Petronella Oortman
Amsterdam ca 1686-1710
Oak inlaid with tortoise shell and tin;
255 x 189,5 x 78 cm

La maison de poupée de Petronella Oortman
Amsterdam env. 1686-1710
En noyer, plaquage d'écaille et d'étain;
255 x 189,5 x 78 cm

Puppenhaus von Petronella Oortman
Amsterdam, zirka 1686-1710
Eiche, beklebt mit Schildkröte und Zinn;
255 x 189,5 x 78 cm

Poppenhuis van Petronella Oortman
Amsterdam ca 1686-1710
Eikenhout belijmd met schildpad en tin:
255 x 189,5 x 78 cm

Support of the dolls' house of Petronella Oortman:
volute leg on ball leg, decorated with leafs

Socle de la maison de poupée de Petronella Oortman:
pied en volute sur pied sphérique orné de feuilles

Unterer Teil Puppenhaus Petronella Oortman:
Volutenornament auf Kugelbein, mit Blättern
verziert

Onderstel poppenhuis Petronella Oortman:
voluutpoot op bolpoot, versierd met bladeren

	53	1	2	3	4	5
	03	10	17	24	31	
	04	11	18	25		
	05	12	19	26		
	06	13	20	27		
	07	14	21	28		
01	08	15	22	29		
02	09	16	23	30		

27 — monday lundi montag maandag

08
09
10
11
12
13
14
15
16
17
18
19
20

28 — tuesday mardi dienstag dinsdag

08
09
10
11
12
13
14
15
16
17
18
19
20

29 — wednesday mercredi mittwoch woensdag

08
09
10
11
12
13
14
15
16
17
18
19
20

30 — thursday jeudi donnerstag donderdag

08
09
10
11
12
13
14
15
16
17
18
19
20

31 — friday vendredi freitag vrijdag

08
09
10
11
12
13
14
15
16
17
18
19
20

01 — saturday samedi samstag zaterdag

New year's day Nouvel an Neujahr Nieuwjaar

02 — sunday dimanche sonntag zondag

2005   53   1   2   3   4   5
03   10   17   24   31
04   11   18   25
05   12   19   26
06   13   20   27
07   14   21   28
01   08   15   22   29
02   09   16   23   30

january | janvier | januar | januari

03 | monday lundi montag maandag

08
09
10
11
12
13
14
15
16
17
18
19
20

04 | tuesday mardi dienstag dinsdag

08
09
10
11
12
13
14
15
16
17
18
19
20

05 | wednesday mercredi mittwoch woensdag

08
09
10
11
12
13
14
15
16
17
18
19
20

06 | thursday jeudi donnerstag donderdag

08
09
10
11
12
13
14
15
16
17
18
19
20

07 | friday vendredi freitag vrijdag

08
09
10
11
12
13
14
15
16
17
18
19
20

08 | saturday samedi samstag zaterdag

09 | sunday dimanche sonntag zondag

1:1

Sidewall of the dolls' house of Petronella Oortman (detail with the mirrored initials of the persons who commissioned the doll's house, Johannes Brandt and Petronella Oortman)

Paroi latérale de la maison de poupée de Petronella Oortman (détail avec les initiales réfléchies des donneurs d'ordre : Johannes Brandt et Petronella Oortman)

Seitenwand Puppenhaus Petronella Oortman (Detail mit gespiegelten Initialen der Auftraggeber Johannes Brandt und Petronella Oortman)

Zijwand poppenhuis Petronella Oortman (detail met de gespiegelde initialen van de opdrachtgevers Johannes Brandt en Petronella Oortman)

Linen room in the dolls' house Petronella Oortman
with linen press and cradle
47.5 x c. 70 x c. 69 cm

Grenier à vêtements de la maison de poupée de
Petronella Oortman avec presse à linge et berceau
47,5 x env. 70 x env. 69 cm

Wäschezimmer auf dem Dachboden im Puppenhaus
Petronella Oortman mit Leinenpresse und
Neugeborenenkörbchen
47,5 x ca. 70 x ca. 69 cm

Kleerzolder poppenhuis Petronella Oortman
met linnenpers en bakermat
47,5 x ca. 70 x ca. 69 cm

january | janvier | januar | januari

2005 53 1 2 3 4 5
03 10 17 24 31
04 11 18 25
05 12 19 26
06 13 20 27
07 14 21 28
01 08 15 22 29
02 09 16 23 30

10 | monday lundi montag maandag

08
09
10
11
12
13
14
15
16
17
18
19
20

11 | tuesday mardi dienstag dinsdag

08
09
10
11
12
13
14
15
16
17
18
19
20

12 | wednesday mercredi mittwoch woensdag

08
09
10
11
12
13
14
15
16
17
18
19
20

13 | thursday jeudi donnerstag donderdag

08
09
10
11
12
13
14
15
16
17
18
19
20

14 | friday vendredi freitag vrijdag

08
09
10
11
12
13
14
15
16
17
18
19
20

15 | saturday samedi samstag zaterdag

16 | sunday dimanche sonntag zondag

2005 53 1 2 3 4 5
03 10 17 24 31
04 11 18 25
05 12 19 26
06 13 20 27
07 14 21 28
01 08 15 22 29
02 09 16 23 30

january | janvier | januar | januari

17 | monday lundi montag maandag

08
09
10
11
12
13
14
15
16
17
18
19
20

18 | tuesday mardi dienstag dinsdag

08
09
10
11
12
13
14
15
16
17
18
19
20

19 | wednesday mercredi mittwoch woensdag

08
09
10
11
12
13
14
15
16
17
18
19
20

20 | thursday jeudi donnerstag donderdag

08
09
10
11
12
13
14
15
16
17
18
19
20

21 | friday vendredi freitag vrijdag

08
09
10
11
12
13
14
15
16
17
18
19
20

22 | saturday samedi samstag zaterdag

23 | sunday dimanche sonntag zondag

Peat and provisions loft
Dolls' house of Petronella Oortman
37 x 35 x 68,5 cm

Grenier à tourbe et grenier à provisions
de la maison de poupée de Petronella Oortman
37 x 35 x 68,5 cm

Dachboden mit Torf- und Vorräten
Puppenhaus Petronella Oortman
37 x 35 x 68,5 cm

Turf- en provisiezolder
Poppenhuis Petronella Oortman
37 x 35 x 68,5 cm

Nursery in the dolls' house of Petronella Oortman
c. 48 x c. 70 x c. 70 cm

Chambre d'enfant de la maison de poupée
de Petronella Oortman
env. 48 x env. 70 x env. 70 cm

Kinderzimmer Puppenhaus Petronella Oortman
ca. 48 x ca. 70 x ca. 70 cm

Kinderkamer poppenhuis Petronella Oortman
ca. 48 x ca. 70 x ca. 70 cm

january | janvier | januar | januari

2005 53 1 2 3 4 5
03 10 17 24 31
04 11 18 25
05 12 19 26
06 13 20 27
07 14 21 28
01 08 15 22 29
02 09 16 23 30

24 | monday lundi montag maandag

08
09
10
11
12
13
14
15
16
17
18
19
20

25 | tuesday mardi dienstag dinsdag

08
09
10
11
12
13
14
15
16
17
18
19
20

26 | wednesday mercredi mittwoch woensdag

08
09
10
11
12
13
14
15
16
17
18
19
20

27 | thursday jeudi donnerstag donderdag

08
09
10
11
12
13
14
15
16
17
18
19
20

28 | friday vendredi freitag vrijdag

08
09
10
11
12
13
14
15
16
17
18
19
20

29 | saturday samedi samstag zaterdag

30 | sunday dimanche sonntag zondag

2005   5   6   7   8   9

07 14 21 28
01 08 15 22
02 09 16 23
03 10 17 24
04 11 18 25
05 12 19 26
06 13 20 27

january **february** | janvier **février** | januar **februar** | januari **februari**

31 | monday lundi montag maandag

08
09
10
11
12
13
14
15
16
17
18
19
20

01 | tuesday mardi dienstag dinsdag

08
09
10
11
12
13
14
15
16
17
18
19
20

02 | wednesday mercredi mittwoch woensdag

08
09
10
11
12
13
14
15
16
17
18
19
20

03 | thursday jeudi donnerstag donderdag

08
09
10
11
12
13
14
15
16
17
18
19
20

04 | friday vendredi freitag vrijdag

08
09
10
11
12
13
14
15
16
17
18
19
20

05 | saturday samedi samstag zaterdag

06 | sunday dimanche sonntag zondag

Children's clothes: shirt and trousers

Vêtements d'enfant : chemise et pantalon

Kinderkleidung: Hemd und Hose

Kinderkleren: hemd en broek

1:1

Children's clothes: two pairs of socks

Vêtements d'enfant : deux paires de bas

Kinderkleidung: zwei Paar Strümpfe

Kinderkleren: twee paar kousen

february | février | februar | februari

2005

	5	6	7	8	9
		07	14	21	28
01	08	15	22		
02	09	16	23		
03	10	17	24		
04	11	18	25		
05	12	19	26		
06	13	20	27		

07 | monday lundi montag maandag

08
09
10
11
12
13
14
15
16
17
18
19
20

08 | tuesday mardi dienstag dinsdag

08
09
10
11
12
13
14
15
16
17
18
19
20

09 | wednesday mercredi mittwoch woensdag

08
09
10
11
12
13
14
15
16
17
18
19
20

10 | thursday jeudi donnerstag donderdag

08
09
10
11
12
13
14
15
16
17
18
19
20

11 | friday vendredi freitag vrijdag

08
09
10
11
12
13
14
15
16
17
18
19
20

12 | saturday samedi samstag zaterdag

13 | sunday dimanche sonntag zondag

2005   5   6   7   8   9

	07	14	21	28
01	08	15	22	
02	09	16	23	
03	10	17	24	
04	11	18	25	
05	12	19	26	
06	13	20	27	

february | février | februar | februari

14 | monday lundi montag maandag

08
09
10
11
12
13
14
15
16
17
18
19
20

15 | tuesday mardi dienstag dinsdag

08
09
10
11
12
13
14
15
16
17
18
19
20

16 | wednesday mercredi mittwoch woensdag

08
09
10
11
12
13
14
15
16
17
18
19
20

17 | thursday jeudi donnerstag donderdag

08
09
10
11
12
13
14
15
16
17
18
19
20

18 | friday vendredi freitag vrijdag

08
09
10
11
12
13
14
15
16
17
18
19
20

19 | saturday samedi samstag zaterdag

20 | sunday dimanche sonntag zondag

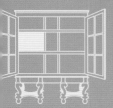

Salon or Best Room in the dolls' house
of Petronella Oortman
c. 55 x 67.5 x c. 69 cm

Salle ou 'belle salle' de la maison
de poupée de Petronella Oortman
env. 55 x 67,5 x env. 69 cm

Saal oder gutes Zimmer
Puppenhaus Petronella Oortman
ca. 55 x 67,5 x ca. 69 cm

Zaal of Beste Kamer
poppenhuis Petronella Oortman
ca. 55 x 67,5 x ca. 69 cm

**Left-hand sidewall of the Salon
in the dolls' house of Petronella
Oortman**
Nicolaas Piemont, Italian landscape
with travellers, oil paint on canvas,
left 51.5 x 23 cm, right 51.5 x 24 cm
Hendrik Wilhelmus (Willem)
van Royen, Flower still life in frame
with monogram, oil paint on canvas,
30 x 18 cm

**Paroi latérale gauche de la salle
de la maison de poupée de
Petronella Oortman**
Nicolaas Piemont, Paysage italien
avec voyageurs, peinture à l'huile
sur toile, à gauche 51,5 x 23 cm,
à droite 51,5 x 24 cm
Hendrik Wilhelmus (Willem) van
Royen, Nature morte de fleurs
encadrée avec monogramme, peinture
à l'huile sur toile, 30 x 18 cm

**Linke Seitenwand des Saales
im Puppenhaus Petronella Oortman**
Nicolaas Piemont, Italienische
Landschaft mit Reisenden,
Ölfarbe auf Tuch, links 51,5 x 23 cm,
rechts 51,5 x 24 cm
Hendrik Wilhelmus (Willem) van
Royen, Stillleben mit Blumen in
Rahmen mit Monogramm, Ölfarbe
auf Tuch, 30 x 18 cm

**Linkerzijwand van de Zaal
poppenhuis Petronella Oortman**
Nicolaas Piemont, Italiaans landschap
met reizigers, olieverf op doek, links
51,5 x 23 cm, rechts 51,5 x 24 cm
Hendrik Wilhelmus (Willem) van
Royen, Bloemstilleven in omlijsting
met monogram, olieverf op doek,
30 x 18 cm

february | février | februar | februari

2005   5   6   7   8   9
            07 14 21 28
    01 08 15 22
    02 09 16 23
    03 10 17 24
    04 11 18 25
    05 12 19 26
    06 13 20 27

21   monday lundi montag maandag

08
09
10
11
12
13
14
15
16
17
18
19
20

22   tuesday mardi dienstag dinsdag

08
09
10
11
12
13
14
15
16
17
18
19
20

23   wednesday mercredi mittwoch woensdag

08
09
10
11
12
13
14
15
16
17
18
19
20

24   thursday jeudi donnerstag donderdag

08
09
10
11
12
13
14
15
16
17
18
19
20

25   friday vendredi freitag vrijdag

08
09
10
11
12
13
14
15
16
17
18
19
20

26   saturday samedi samstag zaterdag

27   sunday dimanche sonntag zondag

07	14	21	28
01	08	15	22	29
02	09	16	23	30
03	10	17	24	31
04	11	18	25
05	12	19	26
06	13	20	27

february **march** | février **mars** | februar **märz** | februari **maart**

28 | monday lundi montag maandag

08
09
10
11
12
13
14
15
16
17
18
19
20

01 | tuesday mardi dienstag dinsdag

08
09
10
11
12
13
14
15
16
17
18
19
20

02 | wednesday mercredi mittwoch woensdag

08
09
10
11
12
13
14
15
16
17
18
19
20

03 | thursday jeudi donnerstag donderdag

08
09
10
11
12
13
14
15
16
17
18
19
20

04 | friday vendredi freitag vrijdag

08
09
10
11
12
13
14
15
16
17
18
19
20

05 | saturday samedi samstag zaterdag

06 | sunday dimanche sonntag zondag

:1

Nicolaas Piemont, Italian landscape with travellers,
il paint on canvas, 51.5 x 23 cm

Nicolaas Piemont, Paysage italien avec voyageurs,
peinture à l'huile sur toile, 51,5 x 23 cm

Nicolaas Piemont, Italienische Landschaft mit
Reisenden, Ölfarbe auf Tuch, 51,5 x 23 cm

Nicolaas Piemont, Italiaans landschap met reizigers,
olieverf op doek, 51,5 x 23 cm

1:1

Hendrik Wilhelmus (Willem) van Royen,
Flower still life in frame with monogram,
oil paint on canvas, 30 x 18 cm

Hendrik Wilhelmus (Willem) van Royen,
Nature morte de fleurs encadrée avec monogramme
peinture à l'huile sur toile, 30 x 18 cm

Hendrik Wilhelmus (Willem) van Royen,
Stillleben mit Blumen in Rahmen mit Monogramm,
Ölfarbe auf Tuch, 30 x 18 cm

Hendrik Wilhelmus (Willem) van Royen,
Bloemstilleven in omlijsting met monogram,
olieverf op doek, 30 x 18 cm

march | mars | märz | maart

2005

	9	10	11	12	13
		07	14	21	28
01	08	15	22	29
02	09	16	23	30
03	10	17	24	31
04	11	18	25	
05	12	19	26	
06	13	20	27	

07 — monday lundi montag maandag

08
09
10
11
12
13
14
15
16
17
18
19
20

08 — tuesday mardi dienstag dinsdag

08
09
10
11
12
13
14
15
16
17
18
19
20

09 — wednesday mercredi mittwoch woensdag

08
09
10
11
12
13
14
15
16
17
18
19
20

10 — thursday jeudi donnerstag donderdag

08
09
10
11
12
13
14
15
16
17
18
19
20

11 — friday vendredi freitag vrijdag

08
09
10
11
12
13
14
15
16
17
18
19
20

12 — saturday samedi samstag zaterdag

13 — sunday dimanche sonntag zondag

2005   9   10   11   12   13
07   14   21   28
01   08   15   22   29
02   09   16   23   30
03   10   17   24   31
04   11   18   25
05   12   19   26
06   13   20   27

14 | monday lundi montag maandag

08
09
10
11
12
13
14
15
16
17
18
19
20

15 | tuesday mardi dienstag dinsdag

08
09
10
11
12
13
14
15
16
17
18
19
20

16 | wednesday mercredi mittwoch woensdag

08
09
10
11
12
13
14
15
16
17
18
19
20

17 | thursday jeudi donnerstag donderdag

08
09
10
11
12
13
14
15
16
17
18
19
20

18 | friday vendredi freitag vrijdag

08
09
10
11
12
13
14
15
16
17
18
19
20

19 | saturday samedi samstag zaterdag

20 | sunday dimanche sonntag zondag

1:1

Hendrik Wilhelmus (Willem) van Royen,
Birds in a park, oil paint on canvas 14 x 12 cm

Hendrik Wilhelmus (Willem) van Royen,
Oiseaux dans un parc,
peinture à l'huile sur toile 14 x 12 cm

Hendrik Wilhelmus (Willem) van Royen,
Vögel im Park, Ölfarbe auf Tuch 14 x 12 cm

Hendrik Wilhelmus (Willem) van Royen,
Vogels in een park, olieverf op doek 14 x 12 cm

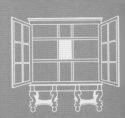

Entrance hall and Study
in the dolls' house of Petronella Oortman
55 x c. 36.5 x c. 66 cm

Maison de devant et Comptoir
de la maison de poupée de Petronella Oortman
55 x env. 36,5 x env. 66 cm

Vorderhaus und Comptoir
Puppenhaus Petronella Oortman
55 x ca. 36,5 x ca. 66 cm

Voorhuis en Comptoir
poppenhuis Petronella Oortman
55 x ca. 36,5 x ca. 66 cm

2005

	9	10	11	12	13
		07	14	21	28
	01	08	15	22	29
	02	09	16	23	30
	03	10	17	24	31
	04	11	18	25	
	05	12	19	26	
	06	13	20	27	

21 monday lundi montag maandag

08
09
10
11
12
13
14
15
16
17
18
19
20

22 tuesday mardi dienstag dinsdag

08
09
10
11
12
13
14
15
16
17
18
19
20

23 wednesday mercredi mittwoch woensdag

08
09
10
11
12
13
14
15
16
17
18
19
20

24 thursday jeudi donnerstag donderdag

08
09
10
11
12
13
14
15
16
17
18
19
20

25 friday vendredi freitag vrijdag

08
09
10
11
12
13
14
15
16
17
18
19
20

26 saturday samedi samstag zaterdag

27 sunday dimanche sonntag zondag

Easter Paques Ostern Pasen

march **april** | mars **avril** | märz **april** | maart **april**

2005   9   10   11   12   13

	07	14	21	28
01	08	15	22	29
02	09	16	23	30
03	10	17	24	31
04	11	18	25	
05	12	19	26	
06	13	20	27	

28 | monday lundi montag maandag

08
09
10
11
12
13
14
15
16
17
18
19
20

29 | tuesday mardi dienstag dinsdag

08
09
10
11
12
13
14
15
16
17
18
19
20

30 | wednesday mercredi mittwoch woensdag

08
09
10
11
12
13
14
15
16
17
18
19
20

31 | thursday jeudi donnerstag donderdag

08
09
10
11
12
13
14
15
16
17
18
19
20

01 | friday vendredi freitag vrijdag

08
09
10
11
12
13
14
15
16
17
18
19
20

02 | saturday samedi samstag zaterdag

03 | sunday dimanche sonntag zondag

'Best' kitchen in the dolls' house
of Petronella Oortman
54.5 x 70 x 69.5 cm

Cuisine d'apparat de la maison
de poupée de Petronella Oortman
54,5 x 70 x 69,5 cm

Prachtküche Puppenhaus Petronella Oortman
54,5 x 70 x 69,5 cm

Pronkkeuken poppenhuis Petronella Oortman
54,5 x 70 x 69,5 cm

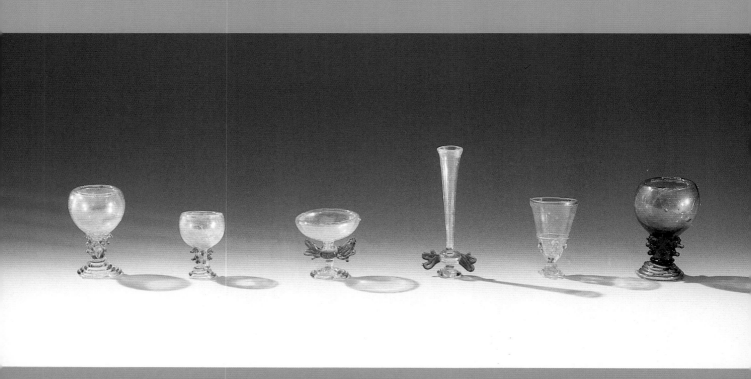

Drinking glasses, flute glasses, comet glasses
and budded beakers

Verres, flûtes, verres comètes et gobelets boutonné

Trinkgläser, Kelchgläser, Kometengläser
und geflochtener Becher

Drinkglazen, fluitglazen, kometenglazen
en geknopte bekertjes

2005

	13	14	15	16	17
	04	11	18	25	
	05	12	19	26	
	06	13	20	27	
	07	14	21	28	
01	08	15	22	29	
02	09	16	23	30	
03	10	17	24		

04 | monday lundi montag maandag

08
09
10
11
12
13
14
15
16
17
18
19
20

05 | tuesday mardi dienstag dinsdag

08
09
10
11
12
13
14
15
16
17
18
19
20

06 | wednesday mercredi mittwoch woensdag

08
09
10
11
12
13
14
15
16
17
18
19
20

07 | thursday jeudi donnerstag donderdag

08
09
10
11
12
13
14
15
16
17
18
19
20

08 | friday vendredi freitag vrijdag

08
09
10
11
12
13
14
15
16
17
18
19
20

09 | saturday samedi samstag zaterdag

10 | sunday dimanche sonntag zondag

april | avril

2005   13 14 15 16 17
04 11 18 25
05 12 19 26
06 13 20 27
07 14 21 28
01 08 15 22 29
02 09 16 23 30
03 10 17 24

11 | monday lundi montag maandag

08
09
10
11
12
13
14
15
16
17
18
19
20

12 | tuesday mardi dienstag dinsdag

08
09
10
11
12
13
14
15
16
17
18
19
20

13 | wednesday mercredi mittwoch woensdag

08
09
10
11
12
13
14
15
16
17
18
19
20

14 | thursday jeudi donnerstag donderdag

08
09
10
11
12
13
14
15
16
17
18
19
20

15 | friday vendredi freitag vrijdag

08
09
10
11
12
13
14
15
16
17
18
19
20

16 | saturday samedi samstag zaterdag

17 | sunday dimanche sonntag zondag

1:1

Three dishes
Arita (Japan) c. 1690-1700

Trois soucoupes
Arita (Japon) env. 1690-1700

Drei Schüsseln
Arita (Japan) ca. 1690-1700

Drie schotels
Arita (Japan) ca. 1690-1700

Tapestry room and Library
in the dolls' house of Petronella Oortman
54.5 x 68.5 x 70 cm

Chambre revêtue de tapisseries et bibliothèque
de la maison de poupée de Petronella Oortman
54,5 x 68,5 x 70 cm

Teppichzimmer und Bibliothek
Puppenhaus Petronella Oortman
54,5 x 68,5 x 70 cm

Tapijtkamer en Bibliotheek
poppenhuis Petronella Oortman
54,5 x 68,5 x 70 cm

2005   13   14   15   16   17

04   11   18   25
05   12   19   26
06   13   20   27
07   14   21   28
01   08   15   22   29
02   09   16   23   30
03   10   17   24

april | avril

18   monday lundi montag maandag

08
09
10
11
12
13
14
15
16
17
18
19
20

19   tuesday mardi dienstag dinsdag

08
09
10
11
12
13
14
15
16
17
18
19
20

20   wednesday mercredi mittwoch woensdag

08
09
10
11
12
13
14
15
16
17
18
19
20

21   thursday jeudi donnerstag donderdag

08
09
10
11
12
13
14
15
16
17
18
19
20

22   friday vendredi freitag vrijdag

08
09
10
11
12
13
14
15
16
17
18
19
20

23   saturday samedi samstag zaterdag

24   sunday dimanche sonntag zondag

2005   13   14   15   16   17

04 11 18 25
05 12 19 26
06 13 20 27
07 14 21 28
01 08 15 22 29
02 09 16 23 30
03 10 17 24

25 | monday lundi montag maandag

08
09
10
11
12
13
14
15
16
17
18
19
20

26 | tuesday mardi dienstag dinsdag

08
09
10
11
12
13
14
15
16
17
18
19
20

27 | wednesday mercredi mittwoch woensdag

08
09
10
11
12
13
14
15
16
17
18
19
20

28 | thursday jeudi donnerstag donderdag

08
09
10
11
12
13
14
15
16
17
18
19
20

29 | friday vendredi freitag vrijdag

08
09
10
11
12
13
14
15
16
17
18
19
20

30 | saturday samedi samstag zaterdag

01 | sunday dimanche sonntag zondag

 1:1

Filled bookcase (detail)

Bibliothèque remplie (détail)

Voller Bücherschrank (Detail)

Gevulde boekenkast (detail)

1:1

Nine books bound in coloured parchment

Neuf livres en reliures de parchemin coloré

Neun Bücher in Bändern aus farbigem Pergament

Negen boeken in banden van gekleurd perkament

may | mai | mei

2005   17 18 19 20 21 22
02 09 16 23 30
03 10 17 24 31
04 11 18 25
05 12 19 26
06 13 20 27
07 14 21 28
01 08 15 22 29

02 | monday lundi montag maandag

08
09
10
11
12
13
14
15
16
17
18
19
20

03 | tuesday mardi dienstag dinsdag

08
09
10
11
12
13
14
15
16
17
18
19
20

04 | wednesday mercredi mittwoch woensdag

08
09
10
11
12
13
14
15
16
17
18
19
20

05 | thursday jeudi donnerstag donderdag

Ascension Day Ascension Himmelfahrt Hemelvaart

08
09
10
11
12
13
14
15
16
17
18
19
20

06 | friday vendredi freitag vrijdag

08
09
10
11
12
13
14
15
16
17
18
19
20

07 | saturday samedi samstag zaterdag

08 | sunday dimanche sonntag zondag

may | mai | mei

2005 17 18 19 20 21 22
02 09 16 23 30
03 10 17 24 31
04 11 18 25
05 12 19 26
06 13 20 27
07 14 21 28
01 08 15 22 29

09 | monday lundi montag maandag

08
09
10
11
12
13
14
15
16
17
18
19
20

10 | tuesday mardi dienstag dinsdag

08
09
10
11
12
13
14
15
16
17
18
19
20

11 | wednesday mercredi mittwoch woensdag

08
09
10
11
12
13
14
15
16
17
18
19
20

12 | thursday jeudi donnerstag donderdag

08
09
10
11
12
13
14
15
16
17
18
19
20

13 | friday vendredi freitag vrijdag

08
09
10
11
12
13
14
15
16
17
18
19
20

14 | saturday samedi samstag zaterdag

15 | sunday dimanche sonntag zondag

Whit Sunday Pentecôte Pfingsten Pinksteren

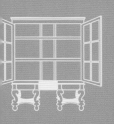

Cellar in the dolls' house of Petronella Oortman
50 x 37,5 x 42 cm

Cave de la maison de poupée de Petronella Oortman
50 x 37,5 x 42 cm

Keller Puppenhaus Petronella Oortman
50 x 37,5 x 42 cm

Kelder poppenhuis Petronella Oortman
50 x 37,5 x 42 cm

1:1

Glass jugs, pots and firepans from the Provisions
loft, Cook room and Cellar in the dolls' house
of Petronella Oortman

Pichets en verre, pots et têts du grenier à provision
cuisine et cave de la maison de poupée de
Petronella Oortman

Gläserne Kannen, Gefäße und Ofenschüsseln
vom Dachboden und aus Küche und Keller
des Puppenhauses von Petronella Oortman

Glazen kannen, potten en testen uit
de Provisiezolder, Kookkeuken en Kelder
poppenhuis Petronella Oortman

may | mai | mei

2005   17 18 19 20 21 22
02 09 16 23 30
03 10 17 24 31
04 11 18 25
05 12 19 26
06 13 20 27
07 14 21 28
01 08 15 22 29

16 | monday lundi montag maandag

8
9
0
1
2
3
4
5
6
7
8
9
0

17 | tuesday mardi dienstag dinsdag

08
09
10
11
12
13
14
15
16
17
18
19
20

18 | wednesday mercredi mittwoch woensdag

08
09
10
11
12
13
14
15
16
17
18
19
20

19 | thursday jeudi donnerstag donderdag

8
9
0
1
2
3
4
5
6
7
8
9
0

20 | friday vendredi freitag vrijdag

08
09
10
11
12
13
14
15
16
17
18
19
20

21 | saturday samedi samstag zaterdag

22 | sunday dimanche sonntag zondag

2005   17 18 19 20 21 22
02 09 16 23 30
03 10 17 24 31
04 11 18 25
05 12 19 26
06 13 20 27
07 14 21 28
01 08 15 22 29

may | mai | mei

23 | monday lundi montag maandag

08
09
10
11
12
13
14
15
16
17
18
19
20

24 | tuesday mardi dienstag dinsdag

08
09
10
11
12
13
14
15
16
17
18
19
20

25 | wednesday mercredi mittwoch woensdag

08
09
10
11
12
13
14
15
16
17
18
19
20

26 | thursday jeudi donnerstag donderdag

08
09
10
11
12
13
14
15
16
17
18
19
20

27 | friday vendredi freitag vrijdag

08
09
10
11
12
13
14
15
16
17
18
19
20

28 | saturday samedi samstag zaterdag

29 | sunday dimanche sonntag zondag

1:1

Four bottles

Quatre bouteilles

Vier Flaschen

Vier flessen

Dolls' house of Petronella Dunois
Amsterdam, c. 1676
Oak, inlaid with walnut, cedar and ebony borders,
200 x 149.5 x 56.5 cm

Maison de poupée de Petronella Dunois
Amsterdam, env. 1676
En chêne, plaquage de noyer, de cèdre
et de filets d'ébène, 200 x 149,5 x 56,5 cm

Puppenhaus von Petronella Dunois
Amsterdam, ca. 1676
Eiche, mit Zedern- und Nussbaumholz furniert,
mit Paspeln aus Ebenholz, 200 x 149,5 x 56,5 cm

Poppenhuis van Petronella Dunois
Amsterdam, ca. 1676
Eikenhout, belijmd met notenhout, cederhout
en biezen van ebbenhout, 200 x 149,5 x 56,5 cm

2005

	22	23	24	25	26
	06	13	20	27
	07	14	21	28
01	08	15	22	29
02	09	16	23	30
03	10	17	24
04	11	18	25
05	12	19	26

30 monday lundi montag maandag

8
9
0
1
2
3
4
5
6
7
8
9
0

31 tuesday mardi dienstag dinsdag

08
09
10
11
12
13
14
15
16
17
18
19
20

01 wednesday mercredi mittwoch woensdag

08
09
10
11
12
13
14
15
16
17
18
19
20

02 thursday jeudi donnerstag donderdag

8
9
0
1
2
3
4
5
6
7
8
9
0

03 friday vendredi freitag vrijdag

08
09
10
11
12
13
14
15
16
17
18
19
20

04 saturday samedi samstag zaterdag

05 sunday dimanche sonntag zondag

2005

22	23	24	25	26
	06	13	20	27
	07	14	21	28
01	08	15	22	29
02	09	16	23	30
03	10	17	24	
04	11	18	25	
05	12	19	26	

06 | monday lundi montag maandag

08
09
10
11
12
13
14
15
16
17
18
19
20

07 | tuesday mardi dienstag dinsdag

08
09
10
11
12
13
14
15
16
17
18
19
20

08 | wednesday mercredi mittwoch woensdag

08
09
10
11
12
13
14
15
16
17
18
19
20

09 | thursday jeudi donnerstag donderdag

08
09
10
11
12
13
14
15
16
17
18
19
20

10 | friday vendredi freitag vrijdag

08
09
10
11
12
13
14
15
16
17
18
19
20

11 | saturday samedi samstag zaterdag

12 | sunday dimanche sonntag zondag

eat loft in the dolls' house
f Petronella Dunois, with servant
6.5 x c. 30 x c. 46 cm

renier à tourbe de la maison de poupée
e Petronella Dunois avec domestique
6.5 x env. 30 x env. 46 cm

achboden mit Torf im Puppenhaus
on Petronella Dunois, mit Knecht
6.5 x ca. 30 x ca. 46 cm

urfzolder poppenhuis
etronella Dunois, met knecht
6.5 x ca. 30 x ca. 46 cm

Linen room in the dolls' house
of Petronella Dunois, with starch maid
36.5 x 61 x c. 46 cm

Grenier à vêtements de la maison de poupée
de Petronella Dunois avec personne chargée
d'amidonner le linge
36,5 x 61 x env. 46 cm

Dachboden mit Wäschekammer
Puppenhaus Petronella Dunois, mit Büglerin
36,5 x 61 x ca. 46 cm

Kleerzolder poppenhuis
Petronella Dunois, met stijfster
36,5 x 61 x ca. 46 cm

2005   22 23 24 25 26

06 13 20 27
07 14 21 28
01 08 15 22 29
02 09 16 23 30
03 10 17 24
04 11 18 25
05 12 19 26

13 | monday lundi montag maandag

08
09
10
11
12
13
14
15
16
17
18
19
20

14 | tuesday mardi dienstag dinsdag

08
09
10
11
12
13
14
15
16
17
18
19
20

15 | wednesday mercredi mittwoch woensdag

08
09
10
11
12
13
14
15
16
17
18
19
20

16 | thursday jeudi donnerstag donderdag

08
09
10
11
12
13
14
15
16
17
18
19
20

17 | friday vendredi freitag vrijdag

08
09
10
11
12
13
14
15
16
17
18
19
20

18 | saturday samedi samstag zaterdag

19 | sunday dimanche sonntag zondag

2005   22 23 24 25 26
06 13 20 27
07 14 21 28
01 08 15 22 29
02 09 16 23 30
03 10 17 24
04 11 18 25
05 12 19 26

june | juin | juni

20 | monday lundi montag maandag

08
09
10
11
12
13
14
15
16
17
18
19
20

21 | tuesday mardi dienstag dinsdag

08
09
10
11
12
13
14
15
16
17
18
19
20

22 | wednesday mercredi mittwoch woensdag

08
09
10
11
12
13
14
15
16
17
18
19
20

23 | thursday jeudi donnerstag donderdag

08
09
10
11
12
13
14
15
16
17
18
19
20

24 | friday vendredi freitag vrijdag

08
09
10
11
12
13
14
15
16
17
18
19
20

25 | saturday samedi samstag zaterdag

26 | sunday dimanche sonntag zondag

Children's clothes: bonnet, jabot and shirt   Kinderkleidung: Mütze, Halskrause und Hemd

Vêtements d'enfant : bonnet, collerette et chemise   Kinderkleren: muts, befje en hemd

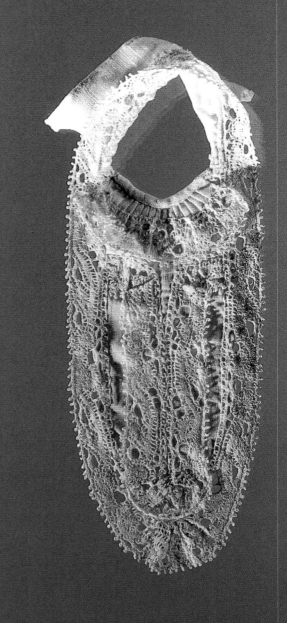

1:1

Children's clothes: apron or pinafore

Vêtements d'enfant : tablier ou plastron

Kinderkleidung: Schürze oder Bruststück

Kinderkleren: voorschoot of borststuk

une **july** | juin **juillet** | juni **juli**

2005
	22	23	24	25	26
	06	13	20	27
01	07	14	21	28
02	08	15	22	29
03	09	16	23	30
04	10	17	24
05	11	18	25
	12	19	26

27 | monday lundi montag maandag

8
9
0
1
2
3
4
5
6
7
8
9
0

28 | tuesday mardi dienstag dinsdag

08
09
10
11
12
13
14
15
16
17
18
19
20

29 | wednesday mercredi mittwoch woensdag

08
09
10
11
12
13
14
15
16
17
18
19
20

30 | thursday jeudi donnerstag donderdag

8
9
0
1
2
3
4
5
6
7
8
9
0

01 | friday vendredi freitag vrijdag

08
09
10
11
12
13
14
15
16
17
18
19
20

02 | saturday samedi samstag zaterdag

03 | sunday dimanche sonntag zondag

2005 26 27 28 29 30
04 11 18 25
05 12 19 26
06 13 20 27
07 14 21 28
01 08 15 22 29
02 09 16 23 30
03 10 17 24 31

july | juillet | juli

04 | monday lundi montag maandag

08
09
10
11
12
13
14
15
16
17
18
19
20

05 | tuesday mardi dienstag dinsdag

08
09
10
11
12
13
14
15
16
17
18
19
20

06 | wednesday mercredi mittwoch woensdag

08
09
10
11
12
13
14
15
16
17
18
19
20

07 | thursday jeudi donnerstag donderdag

08
09
10
11
12
13
14
15
16
17
18
19
20

08 | friday vendredi freitag vrijdag

08
09
10
11
12
13
14
15
16
17
18
19
20

09 | saturday samedi samstag zaterdag

10 | sunday dimanche sonntag zondag

Brushes

Balayettes

Feger

Stoffers

	26	27	28	29	30
		04	11	18	25
		05	12	19	26
		06	13	20	27
		07	14	21	28
01	08	15	22	29
02	09	16	23	30
03	10	17	24	31

11 monday lundi montag maandag

08
09
10
11
12
13
14
15
16
17
18
19
20

12 tuesday mardi dienstag dinsdag

08
09
10
11
12
13
14
15
16
17
18
19
20

13 wednesday mercredi mittwoch woensdag

08
09
10
11
12
13
14
15
16
17
18
19
20

14 thursday jeudi donnerstag donderdag

08
09
10
11
12
13
14
15
16
17
18
19
20

15 friday vendredi freitag vrijdag

08
09
10
11
12
13
14
15
16
17
18
19
20

16 saturday samedi samstag zaterdag

17 sunday dimanche sonntag zondag

2005 26 27 28 29 30
04 11 18 25
05 12 19 26
06 13 20 27
07 14 21 28
01 08 15 22 29
02 09 16 23 30
03 10 17 24 31

18 | monday lundi montag maandag

08
09
10
11
12
13
14
15
16
17
18
19
20

19 | tuesday mardi dienstag dinsdag

08
09
10
11
12
13
14
15
16
17
18
19
20

20 | wednesday mercredi mittwoch woensdag

08
09
10
11
12
13
14
15
16
17
18
19
20

21 | thursday jeudi donnerstag donderdag

08
09
10
11
12
13
14
15
16
17
18
19
20

22 | friday vendredi freitag vrijdag

08
09
10
11
12
13
14
15
16
17
18
19
20

23 | saturday samedi samstag zaterdag

24 | sunday dimanche sonntag zondag

Nursery in the dolls' house of Petronella Dunois,
with four-poster bed, walker and cradle
36.5 x 44 x 46 cm

Chambre d'enfant de la maison de poupée
de Petronella Dunois avec lit à baldaquin,
déambulateur et berceau
36,5 x 44 x 46 cm

Kinderzimmer Puppenhaus Petronella Dunois,
mit Himmelbett, Laufgitter und Wiege
36,5 x 44 x 46 cm

Kinderkamer poppenhuis Petronella Dunois,
met hemelbed, looprek en wieg
36,5 x 44 x 46 cm

 1:1

Nursemaid as seamstress

Bonne d'enfants comme couturière

Kindermädchen als Näherin

Kindermeisje als naaister

july | juillet | juli

2005   26 27 28 29 30
04 11 18 25
05 12 19 26
06 13 20 27
07 14 21 28
01 08 15 22 29
02 09 16 23 30
03 10 17 24 31

25 | monday lundi montag maandag

08
09
10
11
12
13
14
15
16
17
18
19
20

26 | tuesday mardi dienstag dinsdag

08
09
10
11
12
13
14
15
16
17
18
19
20

27 | wednesday mercredi mittwoch woensdag

08
09
10
11
12
13
14
15
16
17
18
19
20

28 | thursday jeudi donnerstag donderdag

08
09
10
11
12
13
14
15
16
17
18
19
20

29 | friday vendredi freitag vrijdag

08
09
10
11
12
13
14
15
16
17
18
19
20

30 | saturday samedi samstag zaterdag

31 | sunday dimanche sonntag zondag

august | août | augustus

2005 31 32 33 34 35
01 08 15 22 29
02 09 16 23 30
03 10 17 24 31
04 11 18 25
05 12 19 26
06 13 20 27
07 14 21 28

01 | monday lundi montag maandag

08
09
10
11
12
13
14
15
16
17
18
19
20

02 | tuesday mardi dienstag dinsdag

08
09
10
11
12
13
14
15
16
17
18
19
20

03 | wednesday mercredi mittwoch woensdag

08
09
10
11
12
13
14
15
16
17
18
19
20

04 | thursday jeudi donnerstag donderdag

08
09
10
11
12
13
14
15
16
17
18
19
20

05 | friday vendredi freitag vrijdag

08
09
10
11
12
13
14
15
16
17
18
19
20

06 | saturday samedi samstag zaterdag

07 | sunday dimanche sonntag zondag

Lying-in room in the dolls' house
of Petronella Dunois
46 x 67.6 x 46 cm

Chambre de l'accouchée de la maison
de poupée de Petronella Dunois
46 x 67,6 x 46 cm

Zimmer mit Neugeborenem,
Puppenhaus Petronella Dunois
46 x 67,6 x 46 cm

Kraamkamer
poppenhuis Petronella Dunois
46 x 67,6 x 46 cm

1:1

Wet nurse with baby in christening napkin

Nounou avec bébé en lange de baptême

Amme mit Baby in Taufwindel

Min met baby in doopluier

august | août | augustus

2005

31	32	33	34	35
01	08	15	22	29
02	09	16	23	30
03	10	17	24	31
04	11	18	25	
05	12	19	26	
06	13	20	27	
07	14	21	28	

08 | monday lundi montag maandag

08
09
10
11
12
13
14
15
16
17
18
19
20

09 | tuesday mardi dienstag dinsdag

08
09
10
11
12
13
14
15
16
17
18
19
20

10 | wednesday mercredi mittwoch woensdag

08
09
10
11
12
13
14
15
16
17
18
19
20

11 | thursday jeudi donnerstag donderdag

08
09
10
11
12
13
14
15
16
17
18
19
20

12 | friday vendredi freitag vrijdag

08
09
10
11
12
13
14
15
16
17
18
19
20

13 | saturday samedi samstag zaterdag

14 | sunday dimanche sonntag zondag

august | août | augustus

2005

31	32	33	34	35
01	08	15	22	29
02	09	16	23	30
03	10	17	24	31
04	11	18	25	
05	12	19	26	
06	13	20	27	
07	14	21	28	

15 | monday lundi montag maandag

08
09
10
11
12
13
14
15
16
17
18
19
20

16 | tuesday mardi dienstag dinsdag

08
09
10
11
12
13
14
15
16
17
18
19
20

17 | wednesday mercredi mittwoch woensdag

08
09
10
11
12
13
14
15
16
17
18
19
20

18 | thursday jeudi donnerstag donderdag

08
09
10
11
12
13
14
15
16
17
18
19
20

19 | friday vendredi freitag vrijdag

08
09
10
11
12
13
14
15
16
17
18
19
20

20 | saturday samedi samstag zaterdag

21 | sunday dimanche sonntag zondag

1:1

Wessel Jansen (active 1642-1696),
standing hearth plates

Wessel Jansen (a travaillé de 1642 à 1696),
contrecoeurs

Wessel Jansen (tätig von 1642-1696),
vertikale Kaminplatten

Wessel Jansen (werkzaam 1642-1696),
staande haardplaten

1:1

Father of the newborn child, dressed in justicoat
and knee breeches made of brown cloth

Mari de l'accouchée vêtu d'un justaucorps
et d'une culotte courte en drap brun

Ehemann der Hebamme, gekleidet in ein
Justaucorps mit Kniehose aus braunem Tuch

Man van de kraamvrouw, gekleed in justaucorps
en kniebroek van bruin laken

august | août | augustus

2005

31	32	33	34	35
01	08	15	22	29
02	09	16	23	30
03	10	17	24	31
04	11	18	25	
05	12	19	26	
06	13	20	27	
07	14	21	28	

22 | monday lundi montag maandag

08
09
10
11
12
13
14
15
16
17
18
19
20

23 | tuesday mardi dienstag dinsdag

08
09
10
11
12
13
14
15
16
17
18
19
20

24 | wednesday mercredi mittwoch woensdag

08
09
10
11
12
13
14
15
16
17
18
19
20

25 | thursday jeudi donnerstag donderdag

08
09
10
11
12
13
14
15
16
17
18
19
20

26 | friday vendredi freitag vrijdag

08
09
10
11
12
13
14
15
16
17
18
19
20

27 | saturday samedi samstag zaterdag

28 | sunday dimanche sonntag zondag

august **september** | août **septembre** | augustus **september**

2005   35   36   37   38   39
05   12   19   26
06   13   20   27
07   14   21   28
01   08   15   22   29
02   09   16   23   30
03   10   17   24
04   11   18   25

29 | monday lundi montag maandag

08
09
10
11
12
13
14
15
16
17
18
19
20

30 | tuesday mardi dienstag dinsdag

08
09
10
11
12
13
14
15
16
17
18
19
20

31 | wednesday mercredi mittwoch woensdag

08
09
10
11
12
13
14
15
16
17
18
19
20

01 | thursday jeudi donnerstag donderdag

08
09
10
11
12
13
14
15
16
17
18
19
20

02 | friday vendredi freitag vrijdag

08
09
10
11
12
13
14
15
16
17
18
19
20

03 | saturday samedi samstag zaterdag

04 | sunday dimanche sonntag zondag

1:1

Cradle with blanket and baby

Berceau avec couverture et bébé

Wiege mit Decke und Baby

Wieg met deken en baby

1:1

Starch maid

Personne qui amidonne le linge

Büglerin

Stijfster

september | septembre | september

2005 35 36 37 38 39
05 12 19 26
06 13 20 27
07 14 21 28
01 08 15 22 29
02 09 16 23 30
03 10 17 24
04 11 18 25

05 | monday lundi montag maandag

08
09
10
11
12
13
14
15
16
17
18
19
20

06 | tuesday mardi dienstag dinsdag

08
09
10
11
12
13
14
15
16
17
18
19
20

07 | wednesday mercredi mittwoch woensdag

08
09
10
11
12
13
14
15
16
17
18
19
20

08 | thursday jeudi donnerstag donderdag

08
09
10
11
12
13
14
15
16
17
18
19
20

09 | friday vendredi freitag vrijdag

08
09
10
11
12
13
14
15
16
17
18
19
20

10 | saturday samedi samstag zaterdag

11 | sunday dimanche sonntag zondag

2005   35   36   37   38   39

05   12   **19**   **26**
06   13   **20**   **27**
07   14   **21**   **28**
01   08   15   **22**   **29**
02   09   16   **23**   **30**
03   10   17   **24**
04   11   18   **25**

september | septembre | september

12 | monday lundi montag maandag

08
09
10
11
12
13
14
15
16
17
18
19
20

13 | tuesday mardi dienstag dinsdag

08
09
10
11
12
13
14
15
16
17
18
19
20

14 | wednesday mercredi mittwoch woensdag

08
09
10
11
12
13
14
15
16
17
18
19
20

15 | thursday jeudi donnerstag donderdag

08
09
10
11
12
13
14
15
16
17
18
19
20

16 | friday vendredi freitag vrijdag

08
09
10
11
12
13
14
15
16
17
18
19
20

17 | saturday samedi samstag zaterdag

18 | sunday dimanche sonntag zondag

Salon or Best Room
in the dolls' house of Petronella Dunois
45 x 67.8 x 46 cm

Salle ou 'belle salle'
de la maison de poupée de Petronella Dunois
45 x 67,8 x 46 cm

Saal oder gutes Zimmer
im Puppenhaus Petronella Dunois
45 x 67,8 x 46 cm

Zaal of Beste Kamer
poppenhuis Petronella Dunois
45 x 67,8 x 46 cm

1:1

Vase
Meissen (Germany) c. 1750-1760

Vase
Meissen (Allemagne) env. 1750-1760

Vase
Meissen (Deutschland) ca. 1750-1760

Vaas
Meissen (Duitsland) ca. 1750-1760

05 12 19 26
06 13 20 27
07 14 21 28
01 08 15 22 29
02 09 16 23 30
03 10 17 24
04 11 18 25

19 | monday lundi montag maandag

08
09
10
11
12
13
14
15
16
17
18
19
20

20 | tuesday mardi dienstag dinsdag

08
09
10
11
12
13
14
15
16
17
18
19
20

21 | wednesday mercredi mittwoch woensdag

08
09
10
11
12
13
14
15
16
17
18
19
20

22 | thursday jeudi donnerstag donderdag

08
09
10
11
12
13
14
15
16
17
18
19
20

23 | friday vendredi freitag vrijdag

08
09
10
11
12
13
14
15
16
17
18
19
20

24 | saturday samedi samstag zaterdag

25 | sunday dimanche sonntag zondag

2005   35   36   37   38   39
05   12   19   26
06   13   20   27
07   14   21   28
01   08   15   22   29
02   09   16   23   30
03   10   17   24
04   11   18   25

september **october** | septembre **octobre** | september **oktober**

26 | monday lundi montag maandag

08

09

10

11

12

13

14

15

16

17

18

19

20

27 | tuesday mardi dienstag dinsdag

08

09

10

11

12

13

14

15

16

17

18

19

20

28 | wednesday mercredi mittwoch woensdag

08

09

10

11

12

13

14

15

16

17

18

19

20

29 | thursday jeudi donnerstag donderdag

08

09

10

11

12

13

14

15

16

17

18

19

20

30 | friday vendredi freitag vrijdag

08

09

10

11

12

13

14

15

16

17

18

19

20

01 | saturday samedi samstag zaterdag

02 | sunday dimanche sonntag zondag

Left: anonymous, Woman with raised
right arm
2nd half 19th century
gouache on ivory, frame made of gilt
tin-lead alloy, glass, paper
Right: anonymous, Woman with veil
2nd half 19th century
gouache on ivory, frame made of gilt
tin-lead alloy, glass, paper

À gauche : anonyme, Femme avec
bras droit levé
2e partie du 19e siècle
gouache sur ivoire, cadre en alliage
étain-plomb doré, verre, papier
À droite : anonyme, Femme avec voile
2e partie du 19e siècle
gouache sur ivoire, cadre en alliage
étain-plomb doré, verre, papier

Links: anonym, Frau mit erhobenem
rechten Arm
Zweite Hälfte neunzehntes Jahrhundert
Gouache auf Elfenbein, vergoldeter
Rahmen aus Zinn-/Bleilegierung,
Glas, Papier
Rechts: anonym, Frau mit Schleier
Zweite Hälfte neunzehntes Jahrhundert
Gouache auf Elfenbein, vergoldeter
Rahmen aus Zinn-/Bleilegierung,
Glas, Papier

Links: anoniem, Vrouw met opgeheven
rechterarm
2e helft 19e eeuw
gouache op ivoor, lijst van vergulde
tin-loodlegering, glas, papier
Rechts: anoniem, Vrouw met sluier
2e helft 19e eeuw
gouache op ivoor, lijst van vergulde
tin-loodlegering, glas, papier

1:1

Left: anonymous (from Rafael), Madonna Della Sedia
2nd half 19th century
gouache on ivory, frame made of gilt tin-lead alloy, glass, paper
Right: anonymous (in the style of François Boucher or J.M.A. Lemoine, Girl with flower basket
2nd half 19th century
gouache on ivory, frame made of gilt tin-lead alloy

À gauche : anonyme (inspiré de Raphaël), Madonna Della Sedia
2e moitié du 19e siècle
gouache sur ivoire, cadre en alliage étain-plomb doré, verre, papier
À droite : anonyme (dans le style de François Boucher de J.M.A. Lemoine, Fille avec panier de fleurs
2e moitié du 19e siècle
gouache sur ivoire, cadre en alliage étain-plomb doré, verre, papier

Links: anonym (nach Raphael), Madonna Della Sedia
Zweite Hälfte neunzehntes Jahrhundert
Gouache auf Elfenbein, vergoldeter Rahmen aus Zinn-/Bleilegierung, Glas, Papier
Rechts: anonym (im Stil von François Boucher oder J.M.A. Lemoine, Mädchen mit Blumenkörbchen
Zweite Hälfte neunzehntes Jahrhundert
Gouache auf Elfenbein, vergoldeter Rahmen aus Zinn-/Bleilegierung, Glas, Papier

Links: anoniem (naar Rafaël), Madonna Della Sedia
2e helft 19e eeuw
gouache op ivoor, lijst van vergulde tin-loodlegering, glas, papier
Rechts: anoniem (in de stijl van François Boucher of J.M.A. Lemoine Meisje met bloemenmand
2e helft 19e eeuw
gouache op ivoor, lijst van vergulde tin-loodlegering

2005

	39	40	41	42	43	44
		03	10	17	24	31
		04	11	18	25	
		05	12	19	26	
		06	13	20	27	
		07	14	21	28	
01	08	15	22	29		
02	09	16	23	30		

03 | monday lundi montag maandag

08
09
10
11
12
13
14
15
16
17
18
19
20

04 | tuesday mardi dienstag dinsdag

08
09
10
11
12
13
14
15
16
17
18
19
20

05 | wednesday mercredi mittwoch woensdag

08
09
10
11
12
13
14
15
16
17
18
19
20

06 | thursday jeudi donnerstag donderdag

08
09
10
11
12
13
14
15
16
17
18
19
20

07 | friday vendredi freitag vrijdag

08
09
10
11
12
13
14
15
16
17
18
19
20

08 | saturday samedi samstag zaterdag

09 | sunday dimanche sonntag zondag

2005 39 40 41 42 43 44
03 10 17 24 31
04 11 18 25
05 12 19 26
06 13 20 27
07 14 21 28
01 08 15 22 29
02 09 16 23 30

10 | monday lundi montag maandag

08
09
10
11
12
13
14
15
16
17
18
19
20

11 | tuesday mardi dienstag dinsdag

08
09
10
11
12
13
14
15
16
17
18
19
20

12 | wednesday mercredi mittwoch woensdag

08
09
10
11
12
13
14
15
16
17
18
19
20

13 | thursday jeudi donnerstag donderdag

08
09
10
11
12
13
14
15
16
17
18
19
20

14 | friday vendredi freitag vrijdag

08
09
10
11
12
13
14
15
16
17
18
19
20

15 | saturday samedi samstag zaterdag

16 | sunday dimanche sonntag zondag

Cellar in the dolls' house of Petronella Dunois
37.4 x 37.3 x 46 cm

Cave de la maison de poupée de Petronella Dunois
37.4 x 37,3, x 46 cm

Keller Puppenhaus Petronella Dunois
37,4 x 37,3, x 46 cm

Kelder poppenhuis Petronella Dunois
37,4 x 37,3, x 46 cm

1:1

Barrels, tubs and wooden shoes

Tonneaux, cuves et sabots

Fässer, Holzfässer und Holzschuhe

Vaten, tobbes en klompen

october | octobre | oktober

2005

	39	40	41	42	43	44
	03	10	17	24	31
	04	11	18	25
	05	12	19	26
	06	13	20	27
	07	14	21	28
01	08	15	22	29
02	09	16	23	30

17   monday lundi montag maandag

08
09
10
11
12
13
14
15
16
17
18
19
20

18   tuesday mardi dienstag dinsdag

08
09
10
11
12
13
14
15
16
17
18
19
20

19   wednesday mercredi mittwoch woensdag

08
09
10
11
12
13
14
15
16
17
18
19
20

20   thursday jeudi donnerstag donderdag

08
09
10
11
12
13
14
15
16
17
18
19
20

21   friday vendredi freitag vrijdag

08
09
10
11
12
13
14
15
16
17
18
19
20

22   saturday samedi samstag zaterdag

23   sunday dimanche sonntag zondag

october | octobre | oktober

2005 39 40 41 42 43 44
03 10 17 24 **31**
04 11 18 25
05 12 19 26
06 13 20 27
07 14 21 28
01 08 15 22 29
02 09 16 23 30

24 | monday lundi montag maandag

08
09
10
11
12
13
14
15
16
17
18
19
20

25 | tuesday mardi dienstag dinsdag

08
09
10
11
12
13
14
15
16
17
18
19
20

26 | wednesday mercredi mittwoch woensdag

08
09
10
11
12
13
14
15
16
17
18
19
20

27 | thursday jeudi donnerstag donderdag

08
09
10
11
12
13
14
15
16
17
18
19
20

28 | friday vendredi freitag vrijdag

08
09
10
11
12
13
14
15
16
17
18
19
20

29 | saturday samedi samstag zaterdag

30 | sunday dimanche sonntag zondag

1:1

Wine and beer barrels on a rack

Tonneaux de vin et de bière sur rayonnage

Wein- und Bierfässer im Regal

Wijn- en biervaten op stelling

1:1

Storage jars with herbs

Bocaux contenant des herbes aromatiques

Vorratfässer mit Kräutern

Voorraadpotten met kruiden

2005 44   45   46   47   48

	07	14	21	28
01	08	15	22	29
02	09	16	23	30
03	10	17	24	
04	11	18	25	
05	12	19	26	
06	13	20	27	

31 | monday lundi montag maandag

08
09
10
11
12
13
14
15
16
17
18
19
20

01 | tuesday mardi dienstag dinsdag

08
09
10
11
12
13
14
15
16
17
18
19
20

02 | wednesday mercredi mittwoch woensdag

08
09
10
11
12
13
14
15
16
17
18
19
20

03 | thursday jeudi donnerstag donderdag

8
9
10
11
12
13
14
15
16
17
18

04 | friday vendredi freitag vrijdag

08
09
10
11
12
13
14
15
16
17
18
19
20

05 | saturday samedi samstag zaterdag

06 | sunday dimanche sonntag zondag

november | novembre

2005   44 45 46 47 48
            07 14 21 28
        01 08 15 22 29
        02 09 16 23 30
        03 10 17 24
        04 11 18 25
        05 12 19 26
        06 13 20 27

07 | monday lundi montag maandag

08
09
10
11
12
13
14
15
16
17
18
19
20

08 | tuesday mardi dienstag dinsdag

08
09
10
11
12
13
14
15
16
17
18
19
20

09 | wednesday mercredi mittwoch woensdag

08
09
10
11
12
13
14
15
16
17
18
19
20

10 | thursday jeudi donnerstag donderdag

08
09
10
11
12
13
14
15
16
17
18
19
20

11 | friday vendredi freitag vrijdag

08
09
10
11
12
13
14
15
16
17
18
19
20

12 | saturday samedi samstag zaterdag

13 | sunday dimanche sonntag zondag

1:1

Storage jars with herbs

Bocaux contenant des herbes aromatiques

Vorratfässer mit Kräutern

Voorraadpotten met kruiden

Kitchen in the dolls' house of Petronella Dunois
37.4 x 48.5 x 46 cm

Cuisine de la maison de poupée de Petronella Dunoi
37,4 x 48,5 x 46 cm

Küche Puppenhaus Petronella Dunois
37,4 x 48,5 x 46 cm

Keuken poppenhuis Petronella Dunois
37,4 x 48,5 x 46 cm

2005 44 45 46 47 48
07 14 21 28
01 08 15 22 29
02 09 16 23 30
03 10 17 24
04 11 18 25
05 12 19 26
06 13 20 27

14 | monday lundi montag maandag

15 | tuesday mardi dienstag dinsdag

08
09
10
11
12
13
14
15
16
17
18
19
20

16 | wednesday mercredi mittwoch woensdag

08
09
10
11
12
13
14
15
16
17
18
19
20

17 | thursday jeudi donnerstag donderdag

18 | friday vendredi freitag vrijdag

08
09
10
11
12
13
14
15
16
17
18
19
20

19 | saturday samedi samstag zaterdag

20 | sunday dimanche sonntag zondag

	07	14	21	28
01	08	15	22	29
02	09	16	23	30
03	10	17	24	
04	11	18	25	
05	12	19	26	
06	13	20	27	

21 | monday lundi montag maandag

08
09
10
11
12
13
14
15
16
17
18
19
20

22 | tuesday mardi dienstag dinsdag

08
09
10
11
12
13
14
15
16
17
18
19
20

23 | wednesday mercredi mittwoch woensdag

08
09
10
11
12
13
14
15
16
17
18
19
20

24 | thursday jeudi donnerstag donderdag

08
09
10
11
12
13
14
15
16
17
18
19
20

25 | friday vendredi freitag vrijdag

08
09
10
11
12
13
14
15
16
17
18
19
20

26 | saturday samedi samstag zaterdag

27 | sunday dimanche sonntag zondag

Kitchen in the dolls' house of Petronella Dunois
with doll, depicting a kitchen maid

Cuisine de la maison de poupée de Petronella Dunois
avec poupée représentant une fille de cuisine

Küche Puppenhaus Petronella Dunois mit Puppe,
die ein Küchenmädchen darstellt

Keuken poppenhuis Petronella Dunois met pop,
voorstellende een keukenmeid

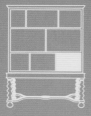

Dining room in the dolls' house of Petronella
Dunois with four dolls, depicting the master's son,
the master, a farmer and a farmer's son
37.4 x 48.2 x 46 cm

Salle à manger de la maison de poupée de Petronella
Dunois avec quatre poupées représentant le fils du
seigneur, le seigneur, un paysan et un fils de paysan
37,4 x 48,2 x 46 cm

Speisesaal Puppenhaus Petronella Dunois mit vier
Puppen, die den Herrn, dessen Sohn, einen Bauern
und dessen Sohn darstellen
37,4 x 48,2 x 46 cm

Eetzaal poppenhuis Petronella Dunois met vier
poppen, voorstellende de zoon van de heer, de heer
een boer en een boerenzoon
37,4 x 48,2 x 46 cm

2005

	48	49	50	51	52
		05	12	19	26
		06	13	20	27
		07	14	21	28
01	08	15	22	29
02	09	16	23	30
03	10	17	24	31
04	11	18	25	

28 | monday lundi montag maandag

08
09
10
11
12
13
14
15
16
17
18
19
20

29 | tuesday mardi dienstag dinsdag

08
09
10
11
12
13
14
15
16
17
18
19
20

30 | wednesday mercredi mittwoch woensdag

08
09
10
11
12
13
14
15
16
17
18
19
20

01 | thursday jeudi donnerstag donderdag

08
09
10
11
12

02 | friday vendredi freitag vrijdag

08
09
10
11
12
13
14
15
16
17
18
19
20

03 | saturday samedi samstag zaterdag

04 | sunday dimanche sonntag zondag

december | décembre | dezember

2005 48 49 50 51 52
05 12 19 26
06 13 20 27
07 14 21 28
01 08 15 22 29
02 09 16 23 30
03 10 17 24 31
04 11 18 25

05 | monday lundi montag maandag

08
09
10
11
12
13
14
15
16
17
18
19
20

06 | tuesday mardi dienstag dinsdag

08
09
10
11
12
13
14
15
16
17
18
19
20

07 | wednesday mercredi mittwoch woensdag

08
09
10
11
12
13
14
15
16
17
18
19
20

08 | thursday jeudi donnerstag donderdag

08
09
10
11
12
13
14
15
16
17
18
19
20

09 | friday vendredi freitag vrijdag

08
09
10
11
12
13
14
15
16
17
18
19
20

10 | saturday samedi samstag zaterdag

11 | sunday dimanche sonntag zondag

1:1

Coiled glasses
Bristol (England) first half 19th century

Verres au pied gravé d'une fine guirlande
Bristol (Angleterre) première moitié du 19e siècle

Pendelgläser, Schlingengläser
Bristol (England), erste Hälfte neunzehntes
Jahrhundert

Slingerglazen
Bristol (Engeland) eerste helft 19e eeuw

1:1

Gentleman, dressed in justicoat and knee breeches
made of brown cloth

Seigneur vêtu d'un justaucorps et d'une culotte
courte en drap brun

Herr, in ein Justaucorps mit Kniehose
aus braunem Tuch gekleidet

Heer, gekleed in justaucorps en kniebroek
van bruin laken

2005 48 49 50 51 52

05 12 19 26
06 13 20 27
07 14 21 28
01 08 15 22 29
02 09 16 23 30
03 10 17 24 31
04 11 18 25

12 | monday lundi montag maandag

08
09
10
11
12
13
14
15
16
17
18
19
20

13 | tuesday mardi dienstag dinsdag

08
09
10
11
12
13
14
15
16
17
18
19
20

14 | wednesday mercredi mittwoch woensdag

08
09
10
11
12
13
14
15
16
17
18
19
20

15 | thursday jeudi donnerstag donderdag

08
09
10
11
12
13
14
15
16
17
18
19
20

16 | friday vendredi freitag vrijdag

08
09
10
11
12
13
14
15
16
17
18
19
20

17 | saturday samedi samstag zaterdag

18 | sunday dimanche sonntag zondag

december | décembre | dezember

2005 48 49 50 51 52

	05	12	19	26
	06	13	20	27
	07	14	21	28
01	08	15	22	29
02	09	16	23	30
03	10	17	24	31
04	11	18	25	

19 | monday lundi montag maandag

08
09
10
11
12
13
14
15
16
17
18
19
20

20 | tuesday mardi dienstag dinsdag

08
09
10
11
12
13
14
15
16
17
18
19
20

21 | wednesday mercredi mittwoch woensdag

08
09
10
11
12
13
14
15
16
17
18
19
20

22 | thursday jeudi donnerstag donderdag

08
09
10
11
12
13
14
15
16
17
18
19
20

23 | friday vendredi freitag vrijdag

08
09
10
11
12
13
14
15
16
17
18
19
20

24 | saturday samedi samstag zaterdag

25 | sunday dimanche sonntag zondag

Christmas Noël Weihnachten Kerstmis

1:1

Antwerp School, The Annunciation
17th century
oil paint on alabaster

École d'Anvers, L'Annonciation
17e siècle
peinture à l'huile sur albâtre

Antwerpener Schule, Die Verkündigung
Siebzehntes Jahrhundert
Ölfarbe auf Alabaster

Antwerpse School, De Annunciatie
17e eeuw
olieverf op albast

Devotion print of the Holy Family
Antwerp, c. 1650-1700
Etching on parchment, trimmed with
gouache and gold paint; mounted
behind glass in oak frame, inlaid with
black-coloured pear wood

Estampe devote représentant
la Sainte Famille
Anvers, env. 1650-1700
Gravure à l'eau forte sur parchemin
marquée avec de la gouache et de
la peinture or ; encadrée sous verre
dans un cadre de chêne, plaquage
de poirier coloré en noir

Bittaufdruck der Heiligen Familie
Antwerpen, ca. 1650-1700
Radierung auf Pergament, akzentuiert
mit Gouache und Goldfarbe;
eingerahmt hinter Glas, Rahmen aus
Eichenholz, furniert mit schwarz
gefärbtem Birnbaumholz

Devotieprent van de Heilige Familie
Antwerpen, ca. 1650-1700
Ets op perkament, afgezet met gouache
en goudverf; gevat achter glas in lijs
van eikenhout, belijmd met zwart
gekleurd perenhout

2005

	48	49	50	51	52
	05	12	19	26	
	06	13	20	27	
	07	14	21	28	
01	08	15	22	29	
02	09	16	23	30	
03	10	17	24	31	
04	11	18	25		

26   monday lundi montag maandag

08
09
10
11
12
13
14
15
16
17
18
19
20

27   tuesday mardi dienstag dinsdag

08
09
10
11
12
13
14
15
16
17
18
19
20

28   wednesday mercredi mittwoch woensdag

08
09
10
11
12
13
14
15
16
17
18
19
20

29   thursday jeudi donnerstag donderdag

30   friday vendredi freitag vrijdag

08
09
10
11
12
13
14
15
16
17
18
19
20

31   saturday samedi samstag zaterdag

01   sunday dimanche sonntag zondag

New year's day Nouvel an Neujahr Nieuwjaar

addresses | adresses | adressen

☎

addresses | **adresses** | **adressen**

addresses | adresses | adressen

The Rijksmuseum Diary 2005 is a coproduction of Inmerc bv
in Wormer and the Rijksmuseum in Amsterdam.
All the works shown form part of the collections of the
Rijksmuseum Amsterdam.

L'Agenda Rijksmuseum 2005 est édité par Inmerc bv, Wormer
en collaboration avec le Rijksmuseum, Amsterdam.
Toutes les oeuvres reproduites font partie des collections
du Rijksmuseum Amsterdam.

Der Terminkalender Rijksmuseum 2005 ist eine Ausgabe
von Inmerc bv in Wormer in Zusammenarbeit mit dem
Rijksmuseum in Amsterdam.
Alle abgebildeten Werke gehören zur Sammlung des
Rijksmuseum Amsterdam.

De Rijksmuseum Agenda 2005 is een uitgave van
Inmerc bv te Wormer in samenwerking met het Rijksmuseum
in Amsterdam.
Alle afgebeelde werken maken deel uit van de collecties
van het Rijksmuseum Amsterdam.

Composition and advice   Composition et conseil
Zusammenstellung und Beratung   Samenstelling en adviezen
Irma Lichtenwagner
Development and production   Développement et production
Entwicklung und Produktion   Ontwikkeling en productie
Inmerc bv, Wormer
Art direction   Conseil artistique
Loek de Leeuw (Inmerc bv)
Design   Graphisme   Gestaltung   Grafisch ontwerp
Impulsar, Krommenie

© This edition   Cette édition   Diese Ausgabe   Deze editie:
2004 Inmerc bv, Wormer
(Netherlands   Pays-Bas   Niederlande)
© Illustrations   Illustrationen   Illustraties:
Rijksmuseum Amsterdam

ISBN 90 6611 469 X
NUR 011, 640